All American Country

Most Songs Not Available Anywhere Else!
Complete Sheet Music Editions

volume 1

Exclusive Distributor to the Music Trade:
CREATIVE CONCEPTS • 967 E. Ojai Ave., Ojai, CA 93023
Exclusive Distributor to the Book Trade:
DOVER PUBLICATIONS, INC. • 180 Varick Street, New York, N.Y. 10014

CONTENTS

BIOGRAPHICAL NOTES...4

SOUVENIR PHOTO SECTION 12

ALL I HAVE TO DO IS DREAM..22

ARE YOU SINCERE?...28

(THE) BATTLE OF NEW ORLEANS 25

(THE) BIRDS AND THE BEES 30

BORN TO LOSE 32

BOWLING GREEN 38

BYE BYE LOVE..40

CHERRY PIE 35

COME LIVE WITH ME...42

DADDY SANG BASS...45

DEEP IN THE HEART OF TEXAS.....................................48

DETROIT CITY 54

DEVOTED TO YOU 56

(THE) DOOR IS STILL OPEN TO MY HEART................58

(THE) END OF THE WORLD...60

EVERYDAY..51

EVERY TIME YOU TOUCH ME (I GET HIGH)................62

FEELIN' SINGLE - SEEIN' DOUBLE...............................65

FOR THE GOOD TIMES...68

FOUR IN THE MORNING...70

GEORGIA ON MY MIND..72

GOT MY MO-JO WORKING..74

(THE) GREAT SPECKLED BIRD..76

GREEN GREEN GRASS OF HOME..................................78

HEY! BABY..80

I'D RATHER BE SORRY...88

IF YOU LOVE ME (LET ME KNOW).................................83

IF YOU'VE GOT THE MONEY (I'VE GOT THE TIME)....90

I LOVE..92

IT KEEPS RIGHT ON A-HURTIN'.....................................95

IT'S JUST A MATTER OF TIME...98

IT WASN'T GOD WHO MADE HONKY TONK ANGELS...............100

CONTENTS

I WILL ALWAYS LOVE YOU 106

JAVA 108

JOLENE 103

JUST ONE LOOK 110

KANSAS CITY 114

KENTUCKY GAMBLER 117

KISS AN ANGEL GOOD MORNIN' 120

LAWDY, MISS CLAWDY 126

LET ME BE THERE 123

(THE) MOST BEAUTIFUL GIRL 128

OLD DOGS, CHILDREN AND WATERMELON WINE 131

ONE DAY AT A TIME 134

ONE HAS MY NAME, THE OTHER HAS MY HEART 138

PAPER ROSES 140

(YOU'VE GOT) PERSONALITY 142

(THE) RACE IS ON 144

ROCKY TOP 150

RUBY, DON'T TAKE YOUR LOVE TO TOWN 152

(A) SATISFIED MIND 154

SHE THINKS I STILL CARE 147

STAY A LITTLE LONGER 158

SWEET THANG 160

TAKE ME BACK TO TULSA 166

(A) THING CALLED LOVE 163

(THE) THREE BELLS 168

(A) VERY SPECIAL LOVE SONG 172

WATERLOO 190

WE COULD 176

WELCOME TO MY WORLD 178

WE'LL SING IN THE SUNSHINE 180

WHEN I LOVED HER 182

WHITE LIGHTNING 184

WILL THE CIRCLE BE UNBROKEN? 186

YOU ARE MY SUNSHINE 190

BIOGRAPHICAL NOTES

ROY ACUFF

Born: September 15, 1903
Hometown: Maynardville, Tennessee

Roy Acuff was the first living artist elected to the Country Music Hall of Fame (1962). He cofounded the Acuff-Rose Publishing Company, the first music publishers devoted exclusively to country music.

Roy grew up in the beautiful Smoky Montains, his father at various times a postmaster, farmer, Baptist minister, and lawyer. Roy played the Jew's harp and harmonica and made fiddles out of cornstalks. At sixteen he was the star athlete at Central High School in Fountain City and acted in everything from Shakespeare to minstrel shows. Small, but cocky, he played semipro ball until the hot July day in 1929 when he collapsed in the outfield from sunstroke. During his two-year recuperation, he improved his fiddle playing and began to sing.

In 1932 he joined a traveling medicine show, then came Roy's own band, Roy Acuff and His Crazy Tennesseans on Knoxville radio stations. In 1936 they recorded "Great Speckled Bird" for Columbia. In 1938, they made their debut on Grand Ole Opry, changing the group's name to the Smoky Mountain Boys.

Acuff is the acknowledged king of country music, and his records have sold into the hundred millions, all over the world. During WWII, Ernie Pyle corroborated Acuff's international fame in a report filed during the battle of Okinawa. The battle cry of a Japanese banzai soldier during an attack: "To hell with President Roosevelt, to hell with Babe Ruth, to hell with Roy Acuff!"

Largely through the business acumen of his wife, Mildred, he has built his immense personal fortune by investing in a number of enterprises, including the Roy Acuff Dunbar Cave Resort near Clarksville, Tennessee. Recently he has been involved with the opening of Opryland, which has become the permanent home of Grand Ole Opry.

Acuff maintains that country music "is down to earth, for the home -- not to get all hepped up and smoke a lot of marijuana and go wild about. The music is full of Christianity and sympathy and understanding. It helps make people better."

LYNN ANDERSON

Born: September 26, 1947
Hometown: Grand Forks, North Dakota

Daughter of Liz Anderson (a successful songwriter) and Casey Anderson (a successful music publisher), she went to Nashville with her mother in 1967 "just for the ride", signed up with Chart Records, fell in love with and married Epic Records biggie Glenn Sutton and had her first hit "Promises, Promises" in 1968. Soon switching over to Columbia Records, she became a regular on the Lawrence Welk Show and won a Grammy in 1971 for Best Female Country Vocal Performance. She made country music history with "I Never Promised You A Rose Garden", which earned a gold record for both the single and the LP. In late 1978, her "Last Love Of My Live" made the Cash Box charts.

Lynn is an accomplished equestrienne, with hundreds of trophies and ribbons in quarter horse competitions. Very much the concerned citizen, she is Youth Advisor for the Tennessee Quarter Horse Association and gives considerable time to raising funds for Easter Seals, Christmas Seals, and Cerebral Palsy.

EDDY ARNOLD

Born: May 15, 1918
Hometown: Henderson, Tennessee

The most frequent word you hear about Eddy is *perfectionist.* Known as the Tennessee Ployboy, he is nevertheless the epitome of sleek sophistication, with his well-tailored appearance and smooth style even when singing something as rural as "Cattle Call", one of the thirteen number-one hits in a career that has seen an incredible 70 million records sold.

It's fascinating that this sharecropper's son learned to play the harmonica and guitar while working in the fields with his brothers. His earliest memories are of hard times. When he was only eleven, his father died and he eventually had to quit school to work the farm. At eighteen he landed a job singing on a radio station in Jackson, Tennessee. He worked with Pee Wee King and the Golden West Cowboys for almost three years, then he married Sally Gayhart. Arnold joined station WTJS in Jackson in 1942 where he was a tremendous hit. It wasn't long before he was discovered by Grand Ole Opry and by the time he was thirty years old, he could celebrate his birthday by having had nine top-ten records that year.

Nashville paid its respects to Arnold by electing him to the Country Music Hall of Fame in 1966.

In addition to performing, Arnold is an astute businessman. His interests include real estate, land development, music publishing and food franchising.

BOBBY BARE

Born: April 7, 1935
Hometown: Irontown, Ohio

Bobby started singing professionally in Charleston, West Virginia, at the age of seventeen. In the late fifties, Bobby was at a recording session with his good friend Bill Parsons, where Bill recorded several songs and had Bobby record a couple. At that session Bobby recorded a song called "The American Boy" which was a take-off on Elvis' career.

After that session, Bobby entered the Army and the tapes of the session were sold to Fraternity Records of Cincinnati. The tapes were all listed as Bill Parsons, so when they found the cut "The All American Boy", Harry Carlson of Fraternity Records thought that it was Bill Parsons who had recorded the song. Bobby did not realize this mistake until he heard the song on the radio being billed as Bill Parson's hit. Bobby and Bill remained friends even after the mishap, but to this day the song is still credited to Bill Parsons.

In 1962 Bobby signed with RCA Records and had the first of his hits under his new label with songs called "Shame On Me" and "Detroit City".

JIM ED BROWN

Born: April 1, 1934
Hometown: Sparkman, Arkansas

Jim Ed grew up helping his father tend the family's 160-acre farm and sawmill business. His older sister Maxine was the music buff in the family and she and Jim Ed began singing together at local events. They made their first recording "Looking Back To See" and Cash Box voted the pair Most Promising Vocal Group of 1953. Then Bonnie, his younger sister, joined the group to form the famed country singing group The Browns, whose "Three Bells" topped the million mark. The group joined the Opry in 1963. Two hit singles followed "Scarlet Ribbons" and "The Old Lamplighter".

The Browns performed for the last time together at the Forty-Second Anniversary Show Of The Grand Ole Opry in October 1967. The two sisters retired to care for their families, and Jim Ed moved on to bigger success on his own with such RCA hit singles as "Pop-a-Top", "Bottle Bottle", "Morning", "Angel's Sunday" and Don Junior".

JOHNNY CASH

Born: February 26, 1932
Hometown: Kingsland, Arkansas

Johnny grew up on a farm where he began singing and writing songs in between his chores. During high school he sang at radio station KLCN in Blytheville, Arkansas.

In 1955, following his discharge from the Air Force, he got a job working in Memphis as a salesman. At this time he met guitarist Luther Perkins and bass player Marshall Grant, and Johnny formed the "Tennessee Two". They went to see Sam Phillips, the president of Sun records in Memphis, for an audition. He recorded Johnny's group doing a song Johnny wrote called "Cry, Cry, Cry". It was released and became a hit in the South. In the fall of 1956, Johnny had his first major hit for Sun records with "I Walk The Line".

After a string of hits for Sun, Johnny signed with Columbia records in 1958, and began another long and successful career, which included many hits with his wife, June Carter.

ROY CLARK

Born: April 15, 1933
Hometown: Meaherrin, Virginia

An incredibly versatile musician, he plays guitar, violin, banjo, piano, trumpet, trombone, and drums. Not content with playing, singing and doing comedy routines, he also dances; proof of this came when he wore white tie and tails for a staircase routine on "The Donny & Marie Show", and when he also managed to keep up with Mitzi Gaynor on her 1977 TV special on CBS. A pilot, too, he flies his Mitsubishi prop jet to his 250 annual concerts, including New York's Carnegie Hall. But there's more: Roy's a radio broadcaster, photographer, boat captain, rancher, horse breeder, and president of his own line of low-calorie foods, Roy Clark's Dieter's Choice.

His career began when at age three he discovered his father's banjo. By sixteen, he won the national Country Music Banjo Championship (and won it again the following year). His first number-one record was "Yesterday When I Was Young" for Dot. He has nearly forty LPs to his credit. His cohosting of Hee Haw alone was seen by over 34 million viewers weekly. CMA named him Entertainer of the Year in 1973. One of his proudest achievements was appearing in Public Service TV with Arthur Fiedler and the ninety-piece Boston Pops Orchestra in 1977.

BILLY "CRASH" CRADDOCK

Born: June 16, 1939
Hometown: Greensboro, North Carolina

As an eleven year old, his "stage" was the barn floor, his "guitar" a broomstick, his "audience" the cows, pigs and chickens -- and his older brother Chauncey gave him lessons on a real guitar. That these lessons paid off is evident.

Billy began recording in 1958 for the Date label ("Ah, Poor Little Baby") which got him a contract with Columbia and appearances on Arthur Godfrey's Talent Scouts and Dick Clark's American Bandstand. he was offered parts in movies and roles on Broadway, but he claims to have turned them all down in favor of country music and stockcar racing (hence the nickname Crash).

For Cartwheel Records, he hit the charts three times in a year with "Knock Three Times", "Dream Lover" and "You Better Move On". In 1978 "I Cheated On A Good Woman's Love" and "Hubba Hubba" hit the singles charts.

Billy and his wife, Mae, have three children, Billy, Jr., Steve and April.

SKEETER DAVIS

Born: December 30, 1931
Hometown: Dry Ridge, Kentucky

Born Mary Frances Penick, Skeeter got her nickname as a youngster from her grandfather, who thought she was to active that she buzzed around like a mosquito. When she was in her early twenties, Skeeter appeared on WSM's Grand Ole Opry in Nashville and the Ernest Tubb show with her good friend, Bee Jay (Betty Jack) Davis. In fact, she took Bee Jay's last name and they billed themselves as the Davis Sisters. When Bee Jay died in an auto crash in the mid-fifties, Skeeter was persuaded for several years by Steve Sholes of RCA records to go on as a solo.

In 1960, Skeeter married all-night disc jockey Ralph Emery of WSM, a marriage that lasted only a couple of years. About 1961, she was presented with a song by Sylvia Dee, "The End Of The World". Chet Atkins felt Skeeter should record the song. So she did -- in memory of Bee Jay. In January 1963 it was released and became her biggest hit. Later in 1963, she recorded a Carole King song called "I Can't Stay Mad At You" which was another hit for her.

Today Skeeter lives in Hasville, still records for RCA and continues to travel around the states in Country and Western shows.

BARBARA FAIRCHILD

Born: November 12, 1950
Hometown: Knobel, Arkansas

As a singer-composer, she cut her first record at fifteen, "A Brand New Bed of Roses". A year later she and a friend headed for Nashville, where they met producer Jerry Crutchfield. He listened to their song, advised them to write at least six more, and then come back. Barbara wrote fifteen and Crutchfield signed her with Knapp Records as a writer. Later she signed with Columbia Records where a single entitled "Color My World" hit number nineteen on the national charts. From her third album, which established her as one of the top women vocalists and songwriters in Country music, came her first number one hit single "The Teddy Bear Song".

In 1975 Barbara was nominated Top Female Vocalist by The Academy of Country Music in California.

THE HAGERS

Jim: Born in Chicago, Illinois
John: Born in Chicago, Illinois

The Hagers are identical twins, best known for their appearance on the Hee Haw show. Versatile, if not too forceful, as artists, they can sing country, folk-rock, blues, pop, and musical comedy, and they joke a little, dance, and have very straight long hair. The Hagers appeared first in Chicago's East Street, joined the Buck Owens show and now commute from their homes in Los Angeles to do Hee Haw segments in Nashville. They record for Capitol.

MERLE HAGGARD

Born: March 6, 1937
Hometown: Bakersfield, California

Son of a dust-bowl Okie migrant, Merle's life and artistry reflect the pain and hopes of the thousands who lost everything in the Depression and expected to find paradise in California -- but wound up starving in Hoover Camps. Born in a converted boxcar, Merle started getting into trouble when he was only fourteen. He landed in San Quentin at twenty, with a one-to-fifteen-year sentence for burglary. While there, he heard country singer Johnny Cash, who would later serve as a major source of inspiration to him.

Paroled in 1960, he returned to his family in Bakersfield, dug ditches by day and played and sang country music at night in local saloons. In 1962 he went to Las Vegas as a back-up guitarist for Wynn Stewart and in 1963 he was offered a recording contract by the Tally label. His first record, "All My Friends Are Gonna Be Strangers", led to a contract with Capitol Records.

Haggard formed his own back-up group, The Strangers and achieved a string of country hits including "Swinging Doors", "The Bottle Let Me Down", "Branded Man", "Sing Me Back Home" and "Mama Tried". His major international breakthrough, however, came in 1969 with his controversial recording of "Okie From Muskogee". One of his most touching songs "If We Make It Through December" topped the charts in 1975.

TOM T. HALL

Born: May 25, 1936
Hometown: Olive Hill, Kentucky

Born in the foothills of the Appalachian Mountains, Tom T. Hall began playing guitar and writing songs before he reached ten. His storylike songs were greatly influenced by Ernest Hemingway and by the style of an innovative Olive Hill guitarist named Clayton Delaney.

During the fifties Hall entered Roanoke College as a journalism major and began sending some of his compositions to Nashville publishing companies. His first taste of success came when one his tunes "DJ For A Day" was recorded by Country singer Jimmy Newman. Newman also signed him to a contract with his New Keyes publishing firm, and for nearly a decade Hall wrote songs that were recorded by many of Nashville's leading artists. Ironically, however, Hall achieved major recognition only when an unknown secretary, Jeannie C. Riley, recorded his "Harper Valley P.T.A." and turned it into a worldwide number one hit. After this success Hall's songs were widely recorded and he was signed as an artist by Mercury Records. Since then he has scored with a long string of country hits, several of which have "crossed over" to the national pop charts.

Today Hall and his wife, singer-songwriter Dixie Dean, live in Brentwood, Tennessee and raise cattle and Basset hounds in their spare time.

EMMYLOU HARRIS

Born: April 2, 1949
Hometown: Birmingham, Alabama

She floated around as a folk singer until the Flying Burrito Brothers heard her sing at the Cellar Door in Washington, D.C., in 1971 and asked her to join them. That's when Gram Parsons -- known by some as the doomed genius -- invited her to work on his Warner's album, GP. She traveled with Gram on his spring 1973 tour and that summer assisted on his last LP, "Grievous Angel".

Parson's strange death shook Emmylou, and instead of pursuing her singing career, she returned to Washington and formed her Angelband. But Parsons had left her a legacy -- her voice on his last LP so impressed Warner's that they signed her, and by early 1975, her own "Pieces Of The Sky" established her as a major artist.

In 1976 her second LP, "Elite Hotel", featured songs by Buck Owens, the Beatles, Hank Williams, Gram Parsons, including "One Of These Days". In 1977, "Luxury Liner" was released. Early 1978 started the new year in fine style with "Quarter Moon In A Ten Cent Town" produced by Brian Ahern and with the backing of the Hot Band.

JOHNNY HORTON

Born: April 30, 1929, Tayler, Texas
Died: November 5, 1960

Johnny Horton gave strong indications of becoming a really big country star. As "the singing fisherman" (he reputedly had magic powers with a rod and reel) of Louisiana Hayride, he exhibited the versatility to sing any kind of song. His specialty, however, was honky-tonk, and "I'm A Honky-Tonk Man" was a successful hit of the mid-fifties.

Horton grew up in East Texas, sang in clubs and local radio stations, and caught the eye of Tillman Franks (a first-rate bass player as well as manager who has taken a number of unknowns and guided them to stardom: David Houston and Claude King, among others), who convinced Horton to specialize in saga songs. Franks was right, and "The Battle Of New Orleans", "Sink The Bismarck" and "Springtime In Alaska" all hit the charts in a big way.

Then tragedy struck. Horton was killed in an automobile collision near Milano, Texas, ending his career. Oddly enough, his widow, Billy Jean, was the widow (and second wife) of Hank Williams.

STONEWALL JACKSON

Born: November 6, 1932
Hometown: Tabor City, North Carolina

Stonewall decided to make Country music his career after getting out of the Navy in 1954. The following year he headed for Nashville in his pickup to try to rack the big time. Wess Rose, whose father had given Hank Williams his start, was instrumental in getting Stonewall Grand Ole Opry and Columbia records contracts. Stonewall's records have always done well on the Country charts. His biggest pop number was the million seller "Waterloo" back in 1959. Other records include "Life To Go", "Sadness In A Song" and "Stamp Out Loneliness".

SONNY JAMES

Born: May 1, 1929
Hometown: Hackleburg, Alabama

After several years of being voted among the top five of male country music performers by Billboard, Record World and Cash Box, Sonny was accorded the singular honor of being named Country Music's Male Artist of the Decade by Record World in 1977.

Starting with his multimillion seller "Young Love" in 1956, he has had a string of phenomenal hits. For seven years, every single he released became a national hit. That's twenty-seven number-one records in a row -- the longest string of top records in country music history.

His 200 Years of Country Music album traces the history and basic styles of country music; his phrasing, authentic sound and historic integrity make this a classic. As producer-arranger, he is responsible for three award-winning LPs by Marie Osmond, starting the with multimillion selling "Paper Roses". A multitime Grammy and CMA nominee, he and his group, The Southern Gentlemen, appear regularly on major TV shows, country fairs, rodeos and concert halls across the country.

WAYLON JENNINGS

Born: June 15, 1937
Hometown: Littlefield, Texas.

Seventeen Magazine has called him "the Humphrey Bogart of Country Music". The CMA called him Male Vocalist of the Year for 1975. He and Willie Nelson have given a new meaning to the word "outlaw".

All of this means he's come a long way since the early fifties when he was one of the youngest disc jockeys in radio history (in Littlefield, Texas), moving on eventually to Lubbock, where rock star Buddy Holly invited him to join his group as elecric bass player. Fate kept him from the plane flight that took Buddy Holly's life. A shaken Waylon then formed his own group, The Waylors, appearing in clubs where Chet Atkins happened to hear him and signed him for RCA.

His major hits include "Honky-Tonk Heroes", "Good-Hearted Woman", "Ruby, Don't Take Your Love To Town", "I'm A Ramblin' Man", "Ol' Waylon", and "The Outlaws" with Willie, Jessi, and Tompall Glaser. In 1978, he made country music chart history twice with "Waylon and Willie" and "I've Always Been Crazy".

Waylon", and "The Outlaws" with Willie, Jessi, and Tom Paul Glaser. In 1978, he made country music chart history twice with "Waylon and Willie" and "I've Always Been Crazy".

GEORGE JONES

Born: September 12, 1931
Hometown: Saratoga, Texas

Since 1955, Jones has recorded hit after hit, his number-one songs including "White Lightning", "She Thinks I Still Care", "A Good Year For The Roses", "Walk Through This World With Me". In 1962, 1963, Cash Box and Billboard voted him Number One Male Vocalist. Amazingly, all of his one-hundred-plus albums and countless singles have made the country top ten since 1956.

When his six-year marriage to Tammy Wynette ended, she responded with solo recordings of "D-I-V-O-R-C-E" and "Stand By Your Man", and then the two got together for "Golden Ring" and "Near You" among others on their joint album, "We Go Together". His big 1978 LP was "George Jones: Bartender's Blues". His Possum Holler Club in Nashville has been so successful that now he's opened branches in Topeka, Kansas, and Mobile, Alabama.

DOUG KERSHAW (DOUGLAS JAMES)

Born: January 24, 1936
Hometown: Tiel Ridge, Louisiana

Doug was born in his parents' houseboat at Tiel Ridge, a tiny island two miles off the Louisiana coast. The "Ragin'" Cajun made his first public appearance at age eight, singing and playing the fiddle at a place called The Bucket Of Blood where performers worked behind a protective screen of chicken wire. Doug and his brother Rusty sang and played their way from Louisiana to Nashville and into a Grand Ole Opry contract by the time he was twenty-one. However a volunteer stint in the Army took him away from Nashville for three years. When he returned, few remembered the name it had taken him years to build up.

One day as he sat in his Nashville apartment, flat broke, he started thinking back to early childhood. Before he knew it, he was writing a song that told of those years. The words to "Louisiana Man" came easily. The song solved Doug's financial problems and gave him the confidence to take a good look at himself and the stigma he had felt as being a poor Cajun.

In the late sixties, he and Bob Dylan were the only two guests on Johnny Cash's first TV show, which led to his being signed by Warner Brothers Records. Hits include "The Ragin' Cajun", "Spanish Moss", "Mama Kershaw's Boy", "Alive and Pickin'", and "Flip, Flop & Fly".

KRIS KRISTOFFERSON

Born: June 22, 1936
Hometown: Brownsville, Texas

The son of a military career man, Kristoffer Kristofferson moved with his family to San Mateo, California, during his high school years. While attending college, he began dabbling in the writing of short stories and songs.

During the late fifties, Kris moved to England to study literature at Oxford University, writing two novels and increasingly greater number of songs. His work came to the attention of Tommy Steele's manager, who signed him to a songwriting and recording contract and was able to build somewhat of a reputation for him under the name of Kris Carson.

After receiving his degree at Oxford, Kris entered the military with the intention of making it his career. While playing his songs at an army club one night, one of his buddies suggested he send his material to Marijohn Wilkin in Nashville. As a result, many of his songs were recorded by leading artists. "Help Me Make It Through The Night", "Me & Bobby McGee", "For The Good Times", "Sunday Mornin' Comin' Down", and "Why Me Lord" have all become contemporary standards.

With the encouragement of such leading Country music figures as Johnny Cash and Roger Miller, Kris decided to become a performer as well, debuting in 1970 in Los Angeles. During the seventies he also began an acting career. Today Kris lives in Nashville with his wife, rock star Rita Coolidge.

JERRY LEE LEWIS

Born: September 29, 1935
Hometown: Ferriday, Louisiana

"The Killer" at fourteen made his professional debut, singing and playing for $9.00 at a local Ford dealer. Early in 1957 Jerry Lee signed with Sun Records. His first release was a plodding "Crazy Arms". The song failed and Lewis was puzzled. A friend then took him aside and convinced him that he should cast off all his inhibitions on stage.

Lewis' second single was the red-hot "Whole Lot Of Shakin' Going On". Jerry then went on national television and created a furor with his dynamic stage presence and wildly flowing hair. Like "Shakin'", Jerry Lee's "Great Balls Of Fire" and "Breathless" became million sellers.

The career of Jerry Lee Lewis was in high gear by 1958, but news of his marriage (his third at age 22) to his thirteen-year-old cousin virtually ruined his rock-and-roll career. Undaunted, Lewis switched to country music, where today he is a super-star and is selling records almost as fast as he did during those frantic Sun days.

ANNE MURRAY

Born: June 20, 1947
Hometown: Springhill, Nova Scotia, Canada

The first Canadian woman to achieve a million-selling record in the United States (Joni Mitchell was the second), Anne Murray originally harbored ambitions of becoming a physical education teacher.

Her singing career started when she needed money for a car and auditioned for the Sing Along Jubilee television show. She got the job for the summer, but Brian Ahern (now her producer) offered to produce her as a solo artist on records. This resulted in a contract with Capitol of Canada and two best-selling albums. With the release of a single called "Snowbird", however, Anne achieved an American best seller and the first of a long string of hits.

Anne lives in Toronto. She won't move to southern California or Nashville, despite the obvious business advantages.

WILLIE NELSON

Born: April 30, 1933
Hometown: Abbot, Texas

"The Red-Headed Stranger" traveled a long, hard winding road to superstardom. He learned to play the guitar at six, played in a dancehall band at ten, sold Bibles and vacuum cleaners door to door, joined the air force, and by 1959 was a part-time disc jockey in Fort Worth, Texas.

The first songs he wrote included "Family Bible" and "Night Life". Going to seek his fortune in Nashville in the early sixties, he wrote such hits as "Crazy" for Patsy Cline, "Hello Walls" for Faron Young and "Ain't It Funny How Time Slips Away" for Ray Price. But Nashville liked him as a writer, not as a performer.

During a dozen years in Nashville, he recorded over twenty albums, none of them successful. Part of the reason was the Nashville method of backing a performer with studio musicians who are excellent at instantly picking up on a tune or style -- but who are strangers to the performers and lack the intimacy that comes with traveling and playing together.

In 1972, Willie returned to Texas and found his personal and musical home in Austin. Since then, Willie Nelson has become a cult figure of mythical proportions. His 1976 RCA LP "Outlaws" with Waylon, Jessie, and Tompall was the first country LP ever to go platinum. As a change of pace, in 1978 he did "Georgia On My Mind", "Someone To Watch Over Me" and "Unchained Melody".

Charley Pride proudly gives Willie credit for making him the first black country music star. Tom T. Hall once called him the Shakespear of Country Music.

OLIVIA NEWTON-JOHN

Born: September 26, 1948
Hometown: Cambridge, England

Olivia was raised in Melbourne, Australia, where her father was headmaster of Ormond College. While still at school, she formed a group with three girl friends, calling themselves the Sol Four. It didn't last very long.

During the mid-sixties, she began singing solo at her brother-in-law's coffee-house and entered a talent contest, which sent her to England. There she teamed up with Pat Carroll, another Australian singer, and began appearing regularly on television and in clubs. Then Pat's visa expired and Olivia returned to Australia and cut her first single, Bob Dylan's "If Not For You" which brought her instant international attention. In 1973, "Let me Be There" earned her first Grammy as Best Country Vocalist and since then here awards could fill the walls of a five-room house.

Making her first movie with John Travolta, the spectacular Grease, she has since settled in Malibu, California, with two cars, four dogs, and five horses.

THE OSBORNE BROTHERS

Bobby Osborne: Born December 1931, in Hyden, Kentucky
Sonny Osborne: Born October, 1937 in Hyden, Kentucky

Ever since becoming partners in 1953, Bobby and Sonny Osborne have been setting the woods of bluegrass and country music on fire with their beautiful harmonies, hard-driving mandolin and banjo playing and ability to turn songs about rocky, Tennessee mountain tops and Georgia piney woods into hit numbers.

The brothers were born in the coal mining town of Hyden where their father was a teacher. In 1941 the family moved to Dayton, Ohio, where their musical development actually began. Bobby was learning guitar and Mandolin, Sonny, the banjo (influenced by their father). When Bobby was 17, he started working on Radio WPFB in Ohio and while there joined Ezra Cline and The Lonesome Pine Fiddlers.

In 1951, when Sonny was 14, he began playing over the air waves of WPFB, the same station where Bobby had started earlier. Then came Korea, and Bobby was assigned to the USMC, being sent overseas and awarded a Purple Heart. In 1953, when Bobby was released from the service, they formed a musical team that would make history in the worlds of bluegrass & country music.

"Rocky Top" was released in 1967 (their biggest hit) and they were voted Vocal Group Of The Year in the 1971 Country Music Association Awards Show.

DOLLY PARTON

Born: January 19, 1946
Hometown: Sevierville, Tennessee

Dolly was the fourth of a dozen children born in the foothills of the Smoky Mountains. Although times were rough for her as a youngster, she enjoyed writing songs and singing every chance she could, and by age seven could play a guitar proficiently.

At eighteen she left home for Nashville to pursue a singing career, and in a short while was signed by Monument Records. A few years later she met and married Carl Dean and also met country star Porter Wagoner, who asked her to appear on his road show. She eventually went on to become Wagoner's singing partner until 1974 when she went on to become a solo performer.

Today Dolly is more diversified than ever, embracing both pop and country audiences. Her famously teased hairdo and skin-tight outfits have given her an image of uniqueness that has made her one of the hottest current female vocalists.

RAY PRICE

Born: January 12, 1926
Hometown: Perryville, Texas

The former hillbilly Ray Noble Price was born in Perryville. He grew up listening to Jimmy Rodgers, the Carlisles and others of that variety. When he graduated from Adamson High School he thought about a musical career, but World War II intervened and he spent four years in the service. This was followed by studying veterinary medicine at No. Texas Agricultural College for three and a half years befor chucking it and deciding to become a professional singer. In January 1952 Ray was signed to WMS's Grand Ole Opry program.

His first two offerings were "Talk To Your Heart" and "Don't Let The Stars Get In Your Eyes", followed by "I'll Be There" and "Release Me". It wasn't until 1970 that he really struck pop gold with a top-ten record called "For The Good Times".

CHARLEY PRIDE

Born: March 18, 1938
Hometown: Sledge, Mississippi

Charley Pride achieved worldwide fame during the late sixties as Country music's first black star. Though he showed an early interest in music and bought his first guitar when he was fourteen, Pride's primary interest was baseball. During his teens he joined the Negro American League and played for the Memphis Red Sox. After two years in the army, he settled in Montana, playing for the Birmingham Black Barons, and then briefly played outfield and pitched for the Los Angeles Angels in 1961.

His musical career began in 1963, when he sang a song over a PA system between ball games. This led to a singing job at a club in Helena, Montana, where his act was noticed by Country star Red Sovine. Sovine brought him to the attention of A & R man Chet Atkins, who signed him to a long-term contract with RCA. During the late sixties, Pride achieved a long string of Country hits and, by 1969, his releases were appearing on the national Pop lists as well.

Today Charley Pride and his wife, Roxanne, live in Dallas, Texas. They have three children, Kraig, Dion, and Angela.

CHARLIE RICH

Born: December 12, 1932
Hometown: Colt, Arkansas

As a lover of music during his adolscense, Charlie joined a combo. After graduating from high school, he entered the University of Arkansas as a music major, concentrating on the piano.

Later he enlisted in the air force. There Rich formed his own group, which he called the Velvetones. They played around the base but broke up when Charlie was discharged.

Charlie Rich returned to Arkansas and began farming. Still, music was in his blood. He managed to get some weekend bookings around the Memphis area, and at a small club was heard by a talent scout for Phillips International Records. Rich was signed, but only as a session pianist for Judd Records. (Judd Phillips was the brother of Sam Phillips.) Sam later heard Rich's singing and signed him as a vocalist/pianist to the Phillips International label.

After a trio of singles, Rich hit it big with "Lonely Weekends" in 1960. He continued making records for Phillips International, but it wasn't until his move to Smash Records that Charlie Rich found chart success again with the 1965 rocker, "Mohari Sam".

Today Rich is a highly successful country artist for Epic Records.

KENNY ROGERS

Born: April 21, 1941
Hometown: Houston, Texas

In 1960, a regional hit, "Crazy Feeling", which ultimately sold a million copies nationwide, took Kenny away from Texas and onto Dick Clark's "American Bandstand". From there he joined the New Christy Minstrels and later (with fellow minstrels Mike Settle, Terry Williams and Thelma Camacho) formed The First Edition. When high school buddy Mickey Newberry brought Kenny "Just Dropped In To See What Condition My Condition Is In", The First Edition took it and made their first major hit along with "Ruby (Don't Take Your Love To Town)", "Reuben James" and "Somethin's Burning'".

Later, as a soloist, Kenny signed with United Artists, leading to several major hits: "Love Lifted Me", "Homemade Love", "Laura", and "While The Feeling's Good". But what made him a superstar was "Lucille" in 1977. Kenny played guitar, bass and "enough piano to get me into trouble". He is also an accomplished photographer and takes pride that his picture of Glen Campbell appears on Glen's Southern Nights album.

1978 was a big Kenny Rogers year; he and Dottie West hosted various country TV specials and won CMA Vocal Duo of the Year award.

LINDA RONSTADT

Born: July 15, 1946
Hometown: Tucson, Arizona

Born into a family totally absorbed in music, Linda began singing and playing the guitar as a child. Her grandfather, father, sister, and brother were all musicians and, during high school, she was part of a family trio that made local television appearances and occasionally recorded.

In 1964 Linda traveled to Los Angeles in search of a recording contract. Joining with Bobby Kimmel and Kenny Edwards, she formed a trio called The Stone Poneys and began playing on the L.A. club circuit. This led to a contract with Capitol Records and the release of their debut album, "Stone Poneys", in 1967. This album was followed by two others, "Evergreen" and "Stoney End". By the end of 1968, however, the Poneys disbanded.

Linda assembled a back-up band (which at one time or another contained members of The Eagles) and continued to record for Capitol on a solo basis, scoring with a number of moderate hit singles. In 1973 she changed affiliation to the Asylum label. Her career took a major upturn during the following year, when she recorded one last album for Capitol (which she owed to the company by virtue of her contract) titled "Heart Like A Wheel". This became a best seller, yielding two chart-topping singles "You're No Good" and "When Will I Be Loved" and putting her in great demand for concert appearances.

In December 1976, her "Linda Ronstadt's Greatest Hits" was released. She won a Grammy for Best Female Pop Vocal Performance for "Hasten Down The Wind" — and for the first time, the Playboy Poll named the same artist as Top Female Singer in both Pop and Country categories — Linda Ronstadt.

JOE STAMPLEY

Born: 1944
Hometown: Springhill, Louisiana

Joe Stampley first made the country charts (way down, number seventy-five, but charted nonetheless) with "Take Time To Know Her". Then came "Soul Song" and a chance for success in Country. Stampley, who started recording at fifteen, was the moving force of the rock group The Uniques, who worked for the Paula label. "Not Too Long Ago" sold about half a million records for The Uniques and then the group sold 600,000 copies with "All These Things".

But Joe's roots were not in rock and the break for him in Country came in his hometown: "One day my little boy tole me that the kids were teasing him about liking a girl from Springhill named Quanette McGraw, who sat next to him in the fourth grade. I thought the name as unusual I used it in a song along with the Arkansas town of Smackover." The end result was that "Quanette McGraw from Smackover, Arkansas" sold 35,000 copies and put Stampley into Country.

PORTER WAGONER

Born: August 12, 1932
Hometown: West Plains, Missouri

The "Thin Man From West Plains", as he is called, got his start in his hometown when as a butcher-store clerk his boss put him on the local radio station to sing a few songs and announce the day's bargains.

In the fall of 1951, he moved to a weekly spot on KWTO, Springfield, where in 1952, the Ozark Jubilee was created by the late Red Foley. In 1955, RCA records signed Porter, his first song, "A Satisfied Man", hitting the number one spot. Other hits included "Company's Comin'", "Your Old Love Letters", "The Green, Green Grass Of Home", "Sorry On The Rocks", "I'll Go Down Swinging" and "Skid Row Joe".

By 1957 he was a regular on the Opry; by the early sixties, he had his own syndicated TV show. It was in 1967 that singing partner Norma Jean retired to get married — that's when he found Dolly Parton! Their partnership produced the 1969 Grammy Award for "Just Someone I Used To Know" and the CMA Duet Award for 1971. The partnership lasted until 1974 when Dolly formed her own band and began recording as a soloist.

BOB WILLS

Born: March 6, 1905
Died: 1975

Wills was born on a farm in East Texas. During his long career as a musician and bandleader, he was to organize one of the finest stage and recording bands ever to perform country music, develop his personal talents as a fiddler and singer, and originate what would come to be recognized as one of the major sub-styles of the country music traditions: Western Swing.

Bob's most famous stylistic trademark is perhaps the energetic "Ahh ha" which punctuates his musical personality. The number of musicians in the Texas Playboys (the name Bob bestowed upon his band) varied from ten to twenty-two. He was the first to assemble an orchestra (or band) to play country music, and he was also instrumental in introducing horns and drums to the genre. The fiddles were always the central point of any Bob Wills band. They became his trademark and made up the first "string section" in country music.

Bob Wills was an innovator. He developed an entirely new style of music and built a huge following playing that "western swing" throughout Texas and the entire southwest. He took creativity to extremely high levels with hits like "San Antonio Rose" and today, nearly 30 years after many of his works were first recorded, you can still find Bob Wills and his Texas Playboys on the radio all around the country.

One of Bob's last public appearances was in 1968 when he was initiated as a member of the prestigious Country Music Hall of Fame in Nashville.

FARON YOUNG

Born: February 25, 1932
Hometown: Shreveport, Louisiana

Unlike many country performers, Young was born in a fairly large city, but his father bought a farm when he was very young. As a child he got his first guitar and spend many hours "figuring out chord and fingering with a herd of cattle as an audience". As a student in high school, he formed his own group, playing at school functions, dances and country fairs. He gave up college when Station KWKH asked him to perform, and shortly afterward he joined Louisiana Hayride, where he impressed the star, Webb Pierce. Pierce not only featured Young on the program, but hired him to be one of the singers on his own traveling show. Capitol Records signed him in 1951 and his first two songs "Tattletale Tears" and "Have I Waited Too Long?" brought him national attention. After a stint in the Army, Grand Ole Opry beckoned.

He is in the top ten of artists with the most records on the country hit charts, with many, many on the top-ten lists and a number of number-one hits, too: "Hello, Walls" in 1961, "The Yellow Bandana" and "It's Four In The Morning" (in 1971).

Roy Clark

Elvis Presley

Sonny James

Charlie Rich

Kenny Rogers

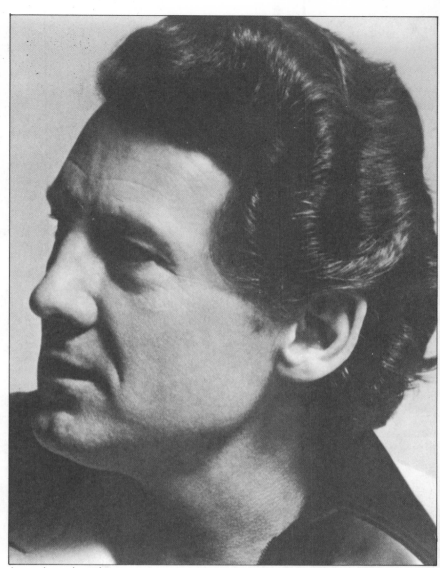

Jerry Lee Lewis

Roy Acuff

George Jones

Kris Kristofferson

Johnny Cash

Jim Reeves

Billy "Crash" Craddock

Dolly Parton

Porter Wagoner

Johnny Horton

Lynn Anderson

The Hagers

Charley Pride

Linda Ronstadt

Faron Young

Waylon Jennings

Emmylou Harris

Willie Nelson

Skeeter Davis

Merle Haggard

Bobby Bare

Tom T. Hall

Jim Ed Brown

Barbara Fairchild

Anne Murray

The Nitty Gritty Dirt Band

Doug Kershaw

Nat Stuckey

The Osborne Brothers

Eddy Arnold

ALL I HAVE TO DO IS DREAM

Words and Music by Boudleaux Bryant

When I want you in my arms, when I want you and all your charms, When-

ev-er I want you,_ All I Have To Do Is Dream,_____ Dream, dream, dream. When

THE BATTLE OF NEW ORLEANS

Words and Music by Jimmy Driftwood

Verse

In eight-een and four-teen we took a lit-tle trip, A-
looked down the riv-er and we seed the Brit-ish come. There

long with Colo-nel Jack-son down the might-y Mis-sis-sip'. We took a lit-tle bac-on and we
must have been a hun-dred of 'em beat-in' on the drum. They stepped_ so_ high_ and they

took a lit-tle beans And we met the blood-y Brit-ish near the town of New Or-leans.
made their bu-gles ring, While we stood be-side our cot-ton bales and did-n't say a thing.

Chorus

We fired our guns and the Brit-ish kept a-com-in'. There wus-n't nigh as man-y as they wus a while a-go. We

ARE YOU SINCERE?

Words and Music by Wayne Walker

THE BIRDS AND THE BEES

Words and Music by Herb Newman

BORN TO LOSE

Words and Music by Ted Daffan

Moderately

Born To Lose, I've lived my life in vain; _____ Ev - 'ry
(Born To) Lose, my ev - 'ry hope is gone; _____ It's so

dream has on - ly brought me pain; _____ All my
hard to face that emp - ty dawn; _____ You were

near; _____ You've grown tired and now you say we're
ness; _____ All my life I've al - ways been so

through; _____ Born To Lose, and now I'm los - in'
blue; _____

you. _____ Born To you. _____

rit.

CHERRY PIE

Words and Music by Joe Josea and Marvin Phillips

BOWLING GREEN

Words and Music by Phil Everly and Terry Slater

BYE BYE LOVE

Words and Music by Felice Bryant and Boudleaux Bryant

COME LIVE WITH ME

Words and Music by Boudleaux and Felice Bryant

DADDY SANG BASS

Words and Music by Carl Perkins

DEEP IN THE HEART OF TEXAS

Words and Music by June Hershey and Don Swander

un - der - stand, And it's there I long to be. _____

Refrain:

The stars at night are big and bright, *Clap, Clap, Clap,
The coy - otes wail a - long the trail,

Clap.

Deep In The Heart Of Tex - as; _____ The prair - ie
Deep In The Heart Of Tex - as; _____ The rab - bits

Clap, Clap, Clap, Clap.

sky is wide and high, Deep In The Heart Of
rush a - round the brush, Deep In The Heart Of

* (Clap hands.)

EVERYDAY

Words and Music by Norman Petty and Charles Hardin

52

DETROIT CITY

Words and Music by Danny Dill and Mel Tillis

Last night I went to sleep in De - troit Cit - y and I dreamed a - bout the cot - ton fields and home; I dreamed a - bout my moth - er, dear old pa - pa, sis - ter and broth - er and I dreamed a - bout the

Home folks think I'm big in De - troit Cit - y, from the let - ters that I write they think I'm fine. But by day I make the cars, by night I make the bars; if on - ly they could

To Coda

Recitation

Cause you know I rode a freight train north to Detroit City.
And after all these years I find I've just been wasting my time,
So I just think I'll take my foolish pride and put it on the south-bound freight and ride
And go on back to the loved ones, the ones that I left waiting so far behind.
I wanna go home, I wanna go home; Oh, how I wanna go home.

DEVOTED TO YOU

Words and Music by Boudleaux Bryant

Dar - ling, you can count on me till the sun dries up the sea Un - til then I'll al - ways be de - vot - ed to you. I'll be yours thru end - less time, I'll a - dore your charms sub - lime. Guess by now you know that I'm de - vot - ed to you.

THE DOOR IS STILL OPEN TO MY HEART

Words and Music by Chuck Willis

THE END OF THE WORLD

Lyric by Sylvia Dee, Music by Arthur Kent

EVERY TIME YOU TOUCH ME (I GET HIGH)

Words and Music by Charlie Rich and Billy Sherrill

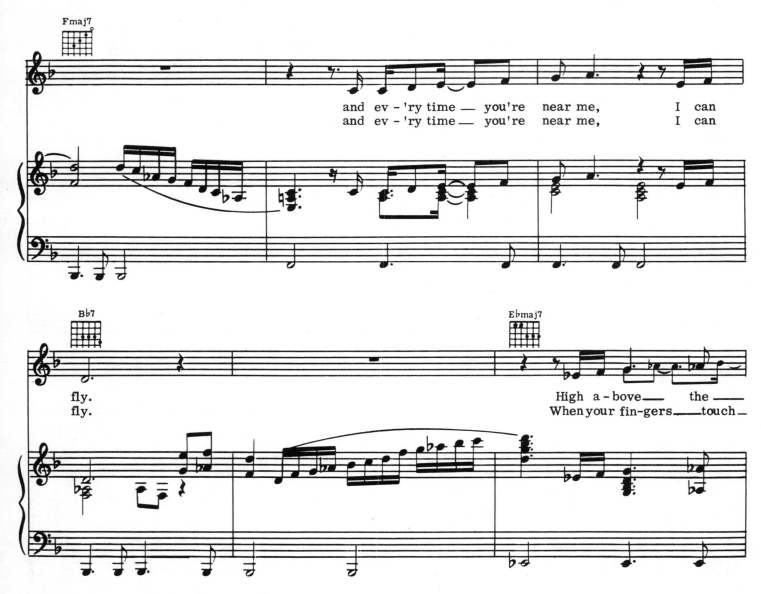

Ev-'ry time you touch me, I get high,
'Cause ev-'ry time you touch me, I get high,

and ev-'ry time — you're near me, I can
and ev-'ry time — you're near me, I can

fly.
fly.

High a-bove — the —
When your fin-gers — touch —

clouds and rain,
my skin,
way a - bove the hurt and pain and
that's when I start to live a - gain, 'cause with-

when you're gone, I fall down from the sky.
out your love, I'd lay lay right down and die.

To Coda ⊕

But ev-ry time — you touch me, I get

high.

I've been touched by the

an-gels, and I've been kissed by the ve - ry best, and I've

been loved __ hard __ by quite a few, __ but af - ter you, __

D. C. al Coda

I for - got the rest. __

Ev - ry time you touch me I get high. __

rit.

Coda

Ped. ------------- *   Ped. --------------------- *

FEELIN' SINGLE - SEEIN' DOUBLE

Words and Music by Wayne Kemp

FOR THE GOOD TIMES

Words and Music by Kris Kristofferson

FOUR IN THE MORNING

Words and Music by Jerry Chestnut

1. It's Four In The Morn-ing and once more the dawn-ing just
2. (I) nev-er de-served her, God knows, when I hurt her, that's the

woke up the want-ing in me;
last thing that I want to do;

Wish-ing I'd nev-er
She tries but she

met her, know-ing if I'd for-get her, how much bet-ter off she would
can't tell how she feels, but I know too well what she's go-in'

3. Last night I told her this time it's all over,
   Making ten times I told her goodbye;
   Last night we broke up, this morning I woke up,
   And for the tenth time I'm changing my mind;
   I saw more love in her eyes when I left her
   Than most foolish men will ever see;
   And it's Four In The Morning and once more the dawning
   Just woke up the wanting in me.

GEORGIA ON MY MIND

Words and Music by Stuart Gorrell and Hoagy Carmichael

GOT MY MO-JO WORKING

Words and Music by Preston Foster

THE GREAT SPECKLED BIRD

Words and Music by Rev. Earl Osborn

GREEN GREEN GRASS OF HOME

Words and Music by Curly Putnam

ADDITIONAL WORDS

(Verse)
The old house is still standing tho' the paint is cracked and dry,
And there's that old oak tree that I used to play on.
Down the lane I walk with my sweet Mary, hair of gold and lips like cherries;
It's good to touch the Green Green Grass Of Home.

(Verse) (recitation, optional)
Then I awake and look around me at the grey walls that surround me
And I realize that I was only dreaming.
For there's a guard, and there's a sad old Padre,
Arm in arm we'll walk at daybreak
Again I'll touch the Green Green Grass Of Home.

(Chorus)
Yes, they'll all come to see me in the shade of that old oak tree
As they lay me 'neath the Green Green Grass Of Home.

HEY! BABY

Words and Music by Cobb and Channel

IF YOU LOVE ME (LET ME KNOW)

Words and Music by John Rostill

Take the chains ——— a - way that keep me lov - in' you.—

The arms that o - pen wide ——— to hold me clos-

er; ——— The hands that run their fin-

gers through my hair; ——— The smile that says hel - lo,—

it's good to see you. Any time I turn a-round to find you there. It's this and so much more that makes me love you. What else can I do to make you see? You

I'D RATHER BE SORRY

Words and Music by Kris Kristofferson

IF YOU'VE GOT THE MONEY (I'VE GOT THE TIME)

Words and Music by Lefty Frizzell and Jim Beck

Brightly

1. IF YOU'VE GOT THE MON-EY, I'VE GOT THE TIME,—— We'll go honk-y
3. " " " " " " " " " " " "

tonk-in' and we'll have a time; We'll make all the night spots,
" " " " " " " " : Bring a-long your Cad-il-lac, Leave

Dance, ro-mance and dine;— IF YOU'VE GOT THE MON-EY, Hon-ey, I'VE GOT THE TIME.
my old wreck be-hind,— " " " " " " " " , " " " " " ".

I LOVE

Words and Music by Tom T. Hall

IT KEEPS RIGHT ON A-HURTIN'

Words and Music by Johnny Tillotson

IT'S JUST A MATTER OF TIME

Words and Music by Clyde Otis, Brook Benton, Belford Hendricks

IT WASN'T GOD WHO MADE HONKY TONK ANGELS

Words and Music by J. D. Miller

Verse:

1. As I sit here to - night, the juke - box play - ing ___
2. (It's a) shame that all the blame is on us wom - en, ___

The tune a - bout the wild side of life; ___
It's not true that on - ly you men feel the same; ___

JOLENE

Words and Music by Dolly Parton

1. Your beau-ty is be-yond com-pare, with flam-ing locks of au - burn hair, with
2. You could have your choice of men but I could nev - er love a - gain.

iv - 'ry skin and eyes of em-'rald green. ___ Your smile is like a breath of spring, your
He's the on - ly one for me, Jo - lene. ___ I had to have this talk with you, my

voice is soft like sum-mer rain, and I can-not com-pete with you, ___ Jo-lene.
hap - pi - ness de-pends on you and what-ev-er you de-cide to do, Jo - lene.

2nd time *D.S. 𝄋 al Coda*

He talks a - bout you in his sleep and there's noth-ing I can do to keep from
Jo -

I WILL ALWAYS LOVE YOU

Words and Music by Dolly Parton

RECITE: I hope life treats you kind, and I hope you have all that you ever dreamed of,
And I wish you joy and happiness, but above all of this, I wish you love.

SING: And I WILL ALWAYS LOVE YOU, I WILL ALWAYS LOVE YOU, I WILL ALWAYS LOVE YOU.
And I WILL ALWAYS LOVE YOU, I WILL ALWAYS LOVE YOU, I WILL ALWAYS LOVE YOU.

JAVA

Words by Jack Wolf and "Bugs" Bower
Music by Freddy Friday, Allen Toussaint and Alvin Tyler

JUST ONE LOOK

Words and Music by G. Carroll and D. Payne

with you.＿＿＿ Oh,＿ oh,＿＿＿ I found out＿
I'm noth-in'＿＿＿ Oh,＿ oh,＿＿＿ just one look＿

how＿ good it fe - ee - eels＿＿ to＿
and I know＿＿ o - ow＿＿ I'll＿

To Coda ⊕

have＿＿ your love.＿＿ Oh,＿ oh,＿＿
get you＿ some - day.＿＿ Oh,＿ oh,＿＿

KANSAS CITY

Words and Music by Jerry Leiber and Mike Stoller

I'm goin' to KAN-SAS CIT-Y; KAN-SAS CIT-Y, Here I come.

I'm goin' to KAN-SAS CIT-Y, KAN-SAS CIT-Y, Here I come.

They got a cra-zy way of lov-in' there and I'm gon-na get me some.

KENTUCKY GAMBLER

Words and Music by Dolly Parton

He want-ed more from life_____ than four kids and a wife_____ and a job in the dark Ken-tuck-y mines, a twen-ty a-cre farm_____ with a shack-y house and barn,_____ that's all he had and all he left be-

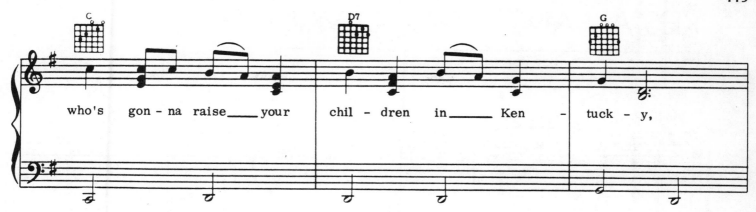

who's gon - na raise____ your chil - dren in ____ Ken - tuck - y,

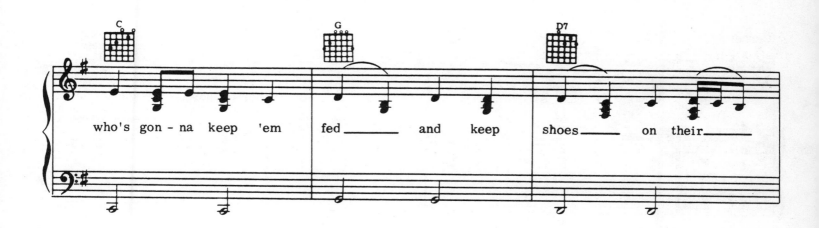

who's gon - na keep 'em fed ____ and keep shoes ____ on their____

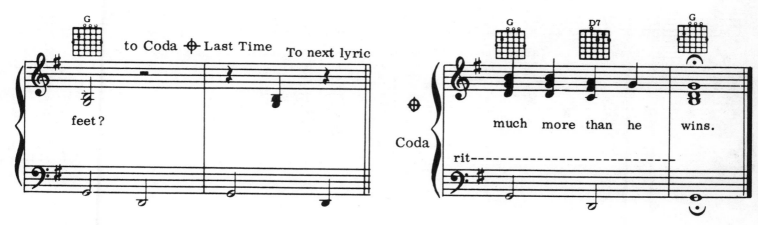

to Coda ⊕ Last Time To next lyric

feet?

Coda

much more than he wins.

rit

2. At gam'bling he was lucky, so he left Kentucky,
   Left behind his woman and his kids.
   Into the gay casino in Nevada's town of Reno,
   Kentucky Gambler planned to get rich quick.

   2nd Chorus: But you have the green - back dollar, sorrow's always bound to follow;
   Reno's dreams fade into neon amber,
   And Lady Luck, she'll lead you on,
   She'll stay awhile and then she's gone.
   You'd better go on home, Kentucky Gambler.

3. At the gambler's paradise, Lady Luck was on his side;
   Kentucky Gambler played his cards just right.
   He won at everything he played, Kentucky Gambler had it made,
   And he should have quit and gone on home that night.

4. But a gambler never seems to stop 'til he loses all he's got,
   And so Kentucky Gambler, he played on, he played 'til he lost all he won.
   He was right back where he started from, then he started wantin' to go home.

   3rd Chorus: Kentucky Gambler, there ain't nobody waitin' in Kentucky
   Where you ran out and someone else walked in.
   Kentucky Gambler, looks like you ain't really very lucky;
   Seems to me a gambler loses much more than he wins.

   (Tag:) Much more than he wins.

KISS AN ANGEL GOOD MORNIN'

Words and Music by Ben Peters

1. When - ev - er I chance to meet some old friends on the street,
2. (Well,) peo - ple may try to guess the se - cret of hap - pi - ness,

They won - der how does a man get to be this way.
But some of them nev - er learn, it's a sim - ple thing.

I've al - ways got a smil - in' face,
The se - cret I'm speak - in' of

LET ME BE THERE

Words and Music by John Rostill

on - ly two can share._____ All I ask_____ you_____

_____ is let me be there._____

2. Watch-ing you grow_____ Let me be_____

All I ask_____ you_____ is let me be there._____

LAWDY, MISS CLAWDY

Words and Music by Lloyd Price

lieve me now ba - by,
sun in the morn - ing
lieve me now ba - by,
'Bye lit - tle dar - lin',

You know I can't be
But don't come home 'till
—— I'm in mis er
You know I can't be
—— Down the road I

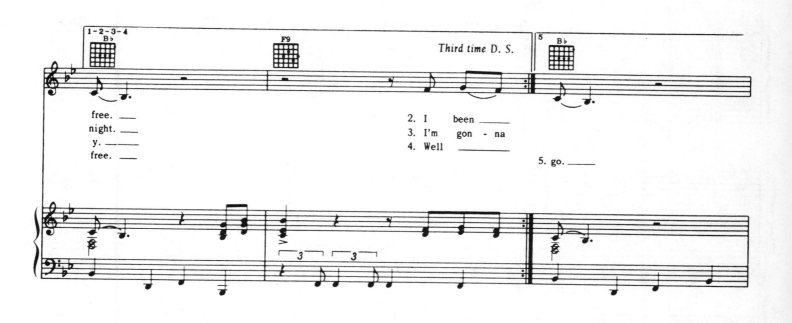

free. ——
night. ——
y. ——
free. ——

Third time D. S.

2. I been ——
3. I'm gon - na
4. Well ——
5. go. ——

Down the road I go. —— Down the road I go.

THE MOST BEAUTIFUL GIRL

Words and Music by Norris Wilson, Billy Sherrill and Rory Bourke

Moderately

Hey, did you hap-pen to see the most beau-ti-ful girl in the world? And if you did was she cry - ing, cry - ing? Hey, if you hap-pen to see the most beau-ti-ful girl that

walked out on me; _____ tell her I'm sor - ry.

Tell her I need _____ my ba - by; won't _____ you

2nd time 𝄋
D. S. and fade

tell her that I love her? (If you) I woke up this morn-

ing, re - al - ized ____ what I had done.

OLD DOGS, CHILDREN AND WATERMELON WINE

Words and Music by Tom T. Hall

3. Ever had a drink of watermelon wine? He asked.
   He told me all about it though I didn't answer back.
   Ain't but three things in this world that's worth a solitary dime,
   But old dogs, children and watermelon wine.

4. He said women think about theyselves when menfolk ain't around,
   And friends are hard to find when they discover that you down.
   He said I tried it all when I was young and in my natural prime;
   Now it's old dogs, children and watermelon wine.

5. Old dogs care about you even when you make mistakes.
   God bless little children while they're still too young to hate.
   When he moved away, I found my pen and copied down that line
   'Bout old dogs and children and watermelon wine.

6. I had to catch a plane up to Atlanta that next day,
   As I left for my room I saw him pickin' up my change.
   That night I dreamed in peaceful sleep of shady summertime
   Of old dogs and children and watermelon wine.

ONE DAY AT A TIME

Words and Music by Kris Kristofferson and Marijohn Wilkin

2. Do you remember when you walked among men
    Well, Jesus, you know if you're looking below that it's worse now than then
    Pushin' and shovin', crowding my mind
    So for my sake, Lord, teach me to take ONE DAY AT A TIME.

ONE HAS MY NAME THE OTHER HAS MY HEART

Words and Music by Eddie Dean, Dearest Dean and Hal Blair

PAPER ROSES

Words and Music by Janice Torre and Fred Spielman

Moderately Slow, with expression

I re-al-ize the way your eyes de-ceived me _____ With

ten-der looks that I mis-took for love; _____ So

take a-way the flow-ers that you gave me _____ And

(YOU'VE GOT) PERSONALITY

Words and Music by Harold Logan and Lloyd Price

THE RACE IS ON

Words and Music by Don Rollins

146

SHE THINKS I STILL CARE

Words and Music by Dickey Lee and Steve Duffy

Freely

Just be-cause I ask a friend a- bout___ her,_____

In Tempo

just be-cause I spoke her name_____ some-where, just be-

cause I saw her then went all to pieces,_____

To Coda

SHE_____ THINKS I STILL CARE. But,

Just be-cause I haunt the same___ old places_____ where the

mem'ry_____ of her lin-gers_____ ev-'ry-where,_____ just be

D.S. al Coda

CODA

Just be-cause I saw her then went all to piec- es_____

SHE THINKS I STILL CARE._____

ROCKY TOP

Words and Music by Boudleaux Bryant and Felice Bryant

1. Wish that I was on ol' ROCK-Y TOP, down in the Tenn-es-see hills;
2. Once two stran-gers climbed ol' ROCK-Y TOP look-in' for a moon-shine still;

Ain't no smog-gy smoke on ROCK-Y TOP; Ain't no tel-e-phone __ bills;
Stran-gers ain't come down from ROCK-Y TOP; Reck-on they nev-er __ will;

Once I had a girl on ROCK-Y TOP; Half bear, oth-er half cat;
Corn won't grow at all on ROCK-Y TOP; Dirt's too rock-y by far;

Verse 3

I've had years of cramped-up city life
Trapped like a duck in a pen;
All I know is it's a pity life
Can't be simple again (CHORUS)

RUBY, DON'T TAKE YOUR LOVE TO TOWN

Words and Music by Mel Tillis

A SATISFIED MIND

Words and Music by Red Hays and Jack Rhodes

Moderately bright tempo

1. How man-y times _____ have you heard some-one say, _____
2. (Once I was) win ning in ____ for-tune and fame; _____

If I had his mon-ey, _____ I would do things my
Ev-'ry-thing that I dreamed for _____ to get a start in life's

Mind. _____ 3. Mon - ey can't buy back your___
4.(When life has) end - ed, my___

youth when you're old, _____ Or a friend when you're lone - ly _____
time has run out, _____ My friends and my loved ones _____

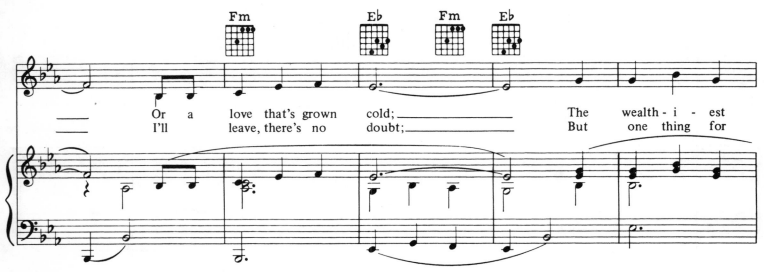

_____ Or a love that's grown cold; _____ The wealth - i - est
_____ I'll leave, there's no doubt; _____ But one thing for

STAY A LITTLE LONGER

Words and Music by Tommy Duncan

With Vigor

1. You ought to see my blue-eyed Sal-ly, She lives a-way down on
2. You cain't get home if you're go-in' by the mill, 'Cause the bridge washed out at the
3. — Set-tin' in the win-dow, Sing-in' to my love, __ A trash buck-et fell from the
4. — Grab your gal and pat her on the head, __ If she don't like bis-cuits

Shin-bone al-ley; The num-ber on the gate, the num-ber on the door And the
bot-tom of the hill; The big creek's up and the big creek's lev-el,
win-dow up a-bove; — Mule and a grass-hop-per eat-in' ice-cream, And the
feed her corn bread, The girls on big creek a-bout half grown, jump

next house o - ver is a gro - c'ry store.
plow my corn __ with the dou - ble shov - el.
mule got sick __ and we laid him on a bean.
on a man __ like a dog on a bone.

Stay all night Stay A Lit - tle Long - er,

Dance all night, And dance a lit - tle long - er, Pull off your coat And throw it in the cor - ner,

Don't see why you don't Stay A Lit - tle Long - er. _____ 2. You _____

SWEET THANG

Words and Music by Nat Stuckey

A THING CALLED LOVE

Words and Music by Jerry Reed Hubbard

TAKE ME BACK TO TULSA

Music and Words by Bob Wills and Tommy Duncan

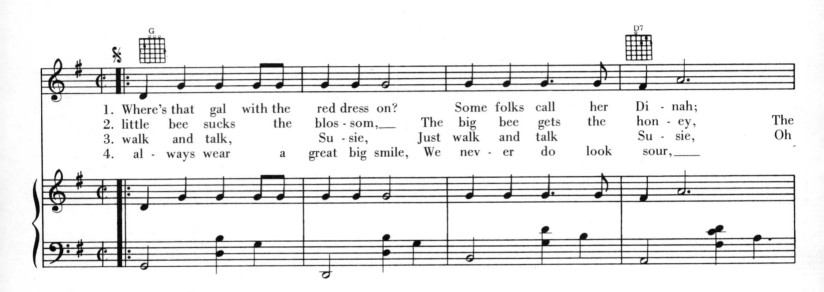

1. Where's that gal with the red dress on? Some folks call her Di - nah; The
2. little bee sucks the blos - som,___ The big bee gets the hon - ey, The
3. walk and talk, Su - sie, Just walk and talk Su - sie, Oh
4. al - ways wear a great big smile, We nev - er do look sour,___

Stole her heart a - way from me, Way down in Lou - i - an - a.
Lit-tle man rais - es cot - ton, The big man gets the mon - ey.
walk and talk_____ Su - sie,_____ Just walk and talk_____ Su - sie.
Trav-el all o'er the coun - try, Play - ing by the hour.____

Refrain:

Take Me Back To Tul - sa, I'm too young to

mar - ry; Take Me Back To Tul - sa, I'm too young to

mar - ry. I'm too young to mar - ry.

THE THREE BELLS

English Lyrics by Bert Reisfeld; Music and French Lyric by Jean Villard (Gilles)

Verse:

1. There's a vil - lage hid - den deep in the val - ley, A - mong the
2. There's a vil - lage hid - den deep in the val - ley, Be - neath the
3. From the vil - lage hid - den deep in the val - ley, One rain - y
1. _____ Vil - la - ge au fond de la val - lé - e, Comme é - ga -

pine trees half for - lorn, And there on a sun - ny morn - ing
moun - tains high a - bove, And there, twen - ty years there - af - ter,
morn - ing dark and gray, A soul winged its way to heav - en,
ré, pres qu'i - gno - re, Voi - ci, dans la nuit é - toi - lé - e, Qu'un

A VERY SPECIAL LOVE SONG

Words and Music by Billy Sherrill and Norris Wilson

WE COULD

Words and Music by Felice Bryant

1. If an-y-one could find the joy that true love brings a girl and boy, ___
2. If an-y-one could ev-er say that their true love was here to stay, ___

WE COULD,   WE COULD, you and I; ___
WE COULD,

WE COULD, you and I; ___   When ___ you're in my

WELCOME TO MY WORLD

Words and Music by Ray Winkler and John Hathcock

WE'LL SING IN THE SUNSHINE

Words and Music by Gale Garnett

WHEN I LOVED HER

Words and Music by Kris Kristofferson

1. Well, she did-n't look as pret-ty as some oth-ers I have known,
   seemed to be so proud of me, just walk-ing, hold-ing hands,
   some of us were born to cast our for-tunes to the wind,

And she was-n't good at con-ver-sa-tion when we were a-lone.
And she did-n't think that mon-ey was the mea-sure of a man.
And I guess I'm bound to tra-vel down a road that nev-er ends.

But she had a way of mak-ing me be-lieve that I be-longed.
And we seemed to fit to-geth-er when I held her in my arms.
But I know I'll nev-er look up-on the likes of her a-gain.

And it felt like com-ing home when I found her.
And it left me feel-ing warm when I loved her.
And I'll nev-er un-der-stand why I lost her. } 'Cause she

WHITE LIGHTNING

Words and Music by J. P. Richardson

1. In North Car-o-li-na 'way back in the hills___ Lived my pap-py and he
2. asked my pap-py why he called his brew___ White light-'ning 'stead of moun-tain
3. ci-ty slick-er came and said, "I'm might-y tough___ I think I want to take that

had 'im a still.___ He brewed white light-ning till the sun went down,___ Then he'd
dew. I took one sip and then I knew___ As my
pow-er-ful stuff." He took one slug, drank it right down___ And I

fill 'im a jug and pass it a-round.___ Might-y, might-y pleas-in', my
eyes bugged out and my face turned blue,___ Light-ning start-ed flash-in',
heard him moan as his head hit the ground,___ "Might-y, might-y pleas-in', your

pap-py's corn squeez-ings called | Whew! _____ | white light-ning. _____
thun-der start - ed crash-ing, | Whew! _____ | white light-ning. _____
pap-py's corn squeez-ings called | Whew! _____ | white light-ning. _____

Tacet

Well, the G men, T men, rev - e - nu - ers, too, Search - ing for the place where he

made his brew. ___ They were look - in', tryin' to book 'im, but my pap - py kept on cook - in'

Tacet

Whew! _____ white light - ning. _____

2. I
3. A

WILL THE CIRCLE BE UNBROKEN?

Words and Music by Sarah Mills

YOU ARE MY SUNSHINE

Words and Music by Jimmie Davis and Charles Mitchell

tak - en _____ and I hung my head and cried: _____
oth - er _____ you'll re - gret it all and some day: _____
oth - er _____ you have shat - tered all my dreams: _____

Chorus:

You Are My Sun - shine _____ my on - ly sun - shine _____ You make me hap - py _____

_____ when skies are gray _____ You'll nev - er know dear _____ how much I love you _____ Please don't

take my sun - shine a - way. _____ 2. I'll al - ways way. _____
3. You told me

WATERLOO

Words and Music by John Loudermilk and Marijohn Wilkin

Chorus

WA-TER-LOO, _____ WA-TER-LOO, _____ Where will you

meet your WA-TER-LOO? _____ Ev-'ry pup-py has its day, _ ev-'ry-

bod-y has to pay, Ev-'ry-bod-y has to meet his WA-TER-LOO. _____ 2. Lit-tle

LOO. _____ 3. Now a fel-lah _____

who's dar-lin' proved un-true, Took her life, But